Contents

A robin on a clock
Focus on: bl, fl, gl, pl, ... 3

Drip, drip, drop!
Focus on: br, cr, dr, fr, gr, tr 8

It is hot!
Focus on: sl, sp, st, sw 14

Skid, smack!
Focus on: sk, sl, sm, sn, st 21

Blends: bl, cl, gl, pl, br, cr, dr, fr, gr, tr, sk, sl, sm, sn, st, sw

Phonemes: s a t p i n m d g o c k ck e u r h b f l j v w x y z q ng

'Tricky' words: a, the, has, yes, no, he, she, oh, for, that, ok, they, says, her, this, to, hi, me, said, of, what, you, was, want, come, sees, asks, do, we

About this book

These short stories are designed to give young children blending and reading practice. They are decodable, which means the words in them only include letter shapes and sounds that the children have learned. The stories also gradually introduce a few 'tricky' words, which are essential for children to become familiar with, such as 'they', 'of' and 'said'.

As children progress through these readers, new letter sounds and 'tricky' words are added and previous learning is revised. The progression links directly to the teaching order in the Letterland teaching range. Each story begins with a title page that provides information for children and teachers.

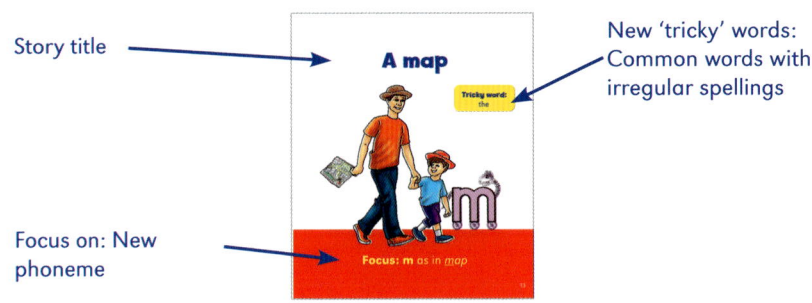

Teaching tips:

- Encourage the sounding out of the decodable words (and any decodable parts of 'tricky' words).
- Discuss the stories with the children to ensure comprehension and engagement.
- Encourage re-reading in pairs or individually to develop fluency and reading for meaning.

A robin on a clock

Tricky words: want, come

Focus on: bl, cl, fl, gl, pl as in _block_, _clock_, _flag_, _glad_, _plug_

Is that a robin on a plum? I want the robin to come in.

It flits to the sill. I am glad.
It fluffs its wings. Will it hop in?

It hops on the blocks. Then it hops on the big, black clock. This is fun!

Then it flits back to the plums.
Let's clap as the robin flaps its wings.

Drip, drip, drop!

Tricky words:
sees, asks

Focus on: br, cr, dr, fr, gr, tr as in
brick, *crab*, *drip*, *frog*, *grin*, *track*

She sees tracks in the sand.
"Did a crab run on the sand? Is that a crab track?" she asks.

She sees a rock. "Is that a frog?" she asks. "Hop, hop, frog!"

She sees a brick. "Is that a bug?" she asks. "It has spots. Rest on that brick, bug!"

Drip, drip, drop! Plip, plip, plop!
The bug runs in a crack. "I am glad it will not get wet in the drips," she said.

She sees lots and lots of drops. The frog and the bug will get a drink.

She claps and grins a big, big grin.

It is hot!

Tricky word: do

Focus on: sl, sp, st, sw
as in _slip, spot, stuck, swim_

"That sun! It is hot!" says Sam. Sam is hot and sad. What can Sam do?

It is hot, but Sam can stop and swim.
Can you swim?

Sam had a swim. Then he slid off.
"It is still hot in the sun!" he says.
What can Sam do?

He spots a bit of wind.
"It is not hot up at the top," says Sam,
"but I am stuck!"
Is Sam stuck? What can Sam do?

"I can swing, then slip off," says Sam.
"I am not stuck! But I am STILL hot!"

"This spot is soft," he says. "And it is not *as* hot!" Sam says. He stops. He is glad.

Skid, smack!

Tricky words:
we, snow

Focus on: sk, sl, sm, sn, st
as in *skate*, *slip*, *smash*, *snap*, *stuck*

"Snow! I am glad!" says Sam.

"We can slip and skid. Let's get the sleds!" says Jim.

"Do not plop in the pond and get wet. Do not slip, skid, bang and get bumps!" Mum says.

They sled and skid on the long hill. What fun!

Can you see the tracks in the snow!
What can you see?

Max wants to skid on the pond.
But he has no skill. He slips.

"Oh, no, no, stop, Max! Stop!"
But Max cannot stop! Skid! Smack!

Max hits the rock. He has no bump, but he has a cut that stings. Can Max fix it?

They help Max stand up. He is a bit stiff.
"Let's stop for a bit," says Max.

"Did you slip, skid, bang and get bumps?" Mum asks.

"Yes, but we still had lots of fun!"

About this series

This series of 8 books accompanies the Letterland teaching range. Each book contains a selection of short stories, featuring the phonic elements listed below. In total there are 30 engaging stories that children can use to decode the 26 most regular alphabet sounds, as well as some 'tricky' high-frequency words.

Book	Focus elements	As in the word...	Story titles
1	**s a t p**	<u>s</u>un, <u>a</u>dd, <u>t</u>ap, <u>p</u>en	Sss! Pat, pat!
2	s a t p **i n m d**	<u>i</u>t, <u>n</u>et, <u>m</u>ap, <u>d</u>og	Sit! Is it Nip? A map Nat is sad
3	s a t p i n m d **g o c k**	<u>g</u>o, <u>o</u>dd, <u>c</u>at, <u>k</u>it	Is it Dan? Tom and Tim Yes or no? Stop!
4	s a t p i n m d g o c k **ck e u r**	<u>duck</u>, <u>e</u>gg, <u>u</u>p, <u>r</u>un	Can he kick? Is Ed a pet? Mop it up! Red Robot runs
5	s a t p i n m d g o c k ck e u r **h b f l**	<u>h</u>en, <u>b</u>at, <u>f</u>an, <u>l</u>eg	A hat for a pet Ben and the cub Huff and puff Leg rest
6	s a t p i n m d g o c k ck e u r h b f l **j v w x**	<u>j</u>et, <u>v</u>an, <u>w</u>ig, bo<u>x</u>	Just jump! At the vet's Wet! Can he fix it?
7	s a t p i n m d g o c k ck e u r h b f l j v w x **y z q ng**	<u>y</u>es, <u>z</u>ip, <u>qu</u>iz, ri<u>ng</u>	Yo-yo Man's yams Zig, zag A quick quiz Ding, dong!
8	**blends** **bl, cl, fl, gl, pl** **br, cr, dr, fr, gr, tr** **sk, sl, sm, sn, sp, st, sw**	<u>bl</u>ock, <u>cl</u>ock, <u>fl</u>ag, <u>gl</u>ad, <u>pl</u>ug <u>br</u>ick, <u>cr</u>ab, <u>dr</u>ip, <u>fr</u>og, <u>gr</u>in t<u>r</u>ack, <u>sk</u>ate, <u>sl</u>ip, <u>sm</u>ash, <u>sn</u>ap, <u>sp</u>ot, <u>st</u>uck, <u>sw</u>im	A robin on a clock Drip, drip, drop! It is hot! Skid, smack!

Collect the sets

Phonics Readers - Red Series

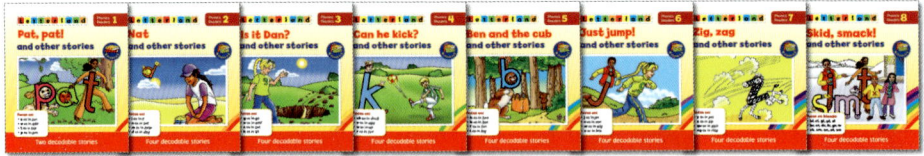

Phonics Readers - Blue Series

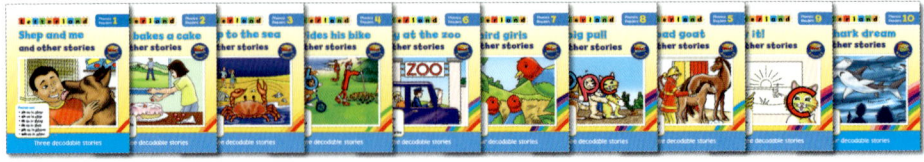

Published by Letterland International Ltd, Leatherhead, Surrey, KT22 9AD, UK
www.letterland.com
ISBN: 978-1-78248-179-9
Product Code: TJ01

© Letterland International 2016
LETTERLAND® is a registered trademark of Lyn Wendon.

First published 2013. This new edition published 2016. Reprinted 2019.
10 9 8 7 6 5 4 3 2

Authors: Stamey Carter and Lisa Holt
Originator of Letterland: Lyn Wendon
Artwork: Nigel Chilvers
Design: Lisa Holt

The author asserts the moral right to be identified as the author of this work. All rights reserved. No part of this publication may be reproduced, stored in a retrieval system, or transmitted in any form or by any means, electronic, mechanical, photocopying, recording or otherwise, without either the prior permission of the Publisher or a licence permitting restricted copying in the United Kingdom issued by the Copyright Licensing Agency Ltd, 90 Tottenham Court Road, London W1T 4LP. This book is sold subject to the condition that it shall not by way of trade or otherwise be lent, hired out or otherwise circulated without the Publisher's prior consent.

Printed in Turkey.